Amy Honeycutt is a relatively new children's book author with a fun and fresh approach to learning the alphabet. Amy and her husband, Joe, have raised three children; Alexis, Jaren, and Abby. They currently live on a small, thirty-acre farm in Ohio where they care for many cows, horses, and even a few mini donkeys. Like many kids, the Honeycutt kids grew up with a love for books and storytime. Their favorite books were the ones that made them laugh. It didn't take long to realize that if you can keep them entertained, you can keep them engaged.

AUSTIN MACAULEY PUBLISHERS™

LONDON • CAMBRIDGE • NEW YORK • SHARJAH

A-Z According to Mikey

Amy Honeycutt

Copyright © Amy Honeycutt (2020)

Ordering Information:

Quantity sales: special discounts are available on quantity purchases by corporations, associations, and others. For details, contact the publisher at the address below.

Publisher's Cataloging-in-Publication data
Honeycutt, Amy
A-Z According to Mikey

ISBN 9781645759959 (Paperback)
ISBN 9781645759942 (Hardback)
ISBN 9781645759966 (ePub e-book)

Library of Congress Control Number: 2020912838
www.austinmacauley.com/us

First Published (2020)
Austin Macauley Publishers LLC
40 Wall Street, 28th Floor
New York, NY 10005
USA
mail-usa@austinmacauley.com
+1 (646) 5125767

I dedicate this book to my loving family. For my husband, Joe, who wholeheartedly believes I can do anything I set my mind to, and for each of my wonderful children whose bold imaginations helped me view the world through the eyes of a child.

Mikey's teacher said, "A is for Apple, B is for Boy, C is for Cat, D is for Dog, and so on. Is that what you learned too?" I thought so... but Mikey started to wonder if may be the alphabet went a bit more like this:

A is for Asher, one of the tallest kids in school, who I heard has a pet alligator named Mr. Cool. Asher's best friend AJ, always brings animal crackers to get Mr. Cool to perform in the pool. I heard he could dolphin kick and dog paddle, he could even swim up for a high five. For the right amount of animal crackers, he's been known to jump into a perfect swan dive.

B is for Baboon, last week I saw one at the zoo. I asked him what his name was, he didn't answer so I named him Big Blue. Then I imagined Blue was in a rock band bouncing up and down on a stage, his best friend Buck Buffalo beside him singing their hit song, "We don't belong in a cage!"

C is for Carrots, that's the name of my dog, who once ate a bucket of crispy chicken, coleslaw, and a silly putty frog! Mom took Carrots to the vet where they gave him medicine for his tummy. Carrots coughed up his lunch, two matchbox cars, and something green and runny.

D is for Doctor Dexter, the best dentist of all. He cleans and counts my teeth in a room with dinosaurs on the wall. Logan Davis said, "He once saw Dr. Dexter dancing to disco and driving a dirt bike, while throwing off a neck tie." I wanted to believe him but sometimes Logan Davis lies.

E is for Echo, my nana's elderly cat, who usually sleeps in the closet on a dirty old ski coat and cap. That crazy cat used to eat eggs and bacon back when she had some teeth, she'd also catch mice and birds running up and down the streets. Nana says that eventually everything gets like that, just look at Echo! She's so old she forgot that she's the neighbor's cat.

F is for Franny Jo Franklin, the fastest girl in my class. She once outran Foster P. Fitzgerald blindfolded and barefoot in the grass. She said, "She was the best, no way she could ever lose. She may have won the foot race, but she'll never know where Foster P. Fitzgerald hid her new red running shoes."

E

F

G is for Galactic Gum, number one among girls and boys. The commercial says, "You'll love this stuff, every pack is sold with a toy!" It must be the best; commercials know kids aren't dumb. Between me and my friends, we have twenty four toys but as far as I know, no one's ever tried the gum.

H is for Hayrides, my favorite time in Fall. Hardman and Haberly's haunted hay rides, scary good fun for one and all. I once did a wicked cool cannon ball right into a blue corn pit, then got lost in the Corn Maze Craze for about an hour. Did I cry? Well...maybe a little bit.

G

Number one among
Girls and Boys.

GALACTIC GUM

GALACTIC GUM

H

Hardman and Haberly's
Haunted Hay Rides

I is for Imaginary igloos, my mom says, "It will have to do. We live in a place called Ivins, where the temperature is regularly one hundred and two." So I imagine my bed is an iceberg far away in an icy sea, where I live alone in an igloo with a sign on the door that reads, 'Please, come visit me'.

J is for Junior Jellyfish, that's what we're called in swim class. Jaxton Jarvis said, "He could swim better than me," and I said,

"If that were true, you'd already be a Sea Bass!" He couldn't think of a single thing to say, not even a little sting. It must have sunk in when he realized we were both poolside, still wearing our water wings.

K is for Karate, stop, chop, and roll! Every Halloween I'm a karate ninja out on candy patrol. My neighborhood's pretty good at handing out candy, except for Mr. and Mrs. Keens. They're afraid some of us kids aren't quite regular, so for some time now, they've been handing out cans of high fiber beans.

L is for Lazy dog, his real name is Duck. He once tried to cross the street, made it part way, needed a nap and was nearly run down by a truck. Now us, neighborhood kids, try to keep track of him. We got together as a group, and currently own and operate 'Lazy Dog Duck' transport and wagon.

K

L

M is for mismatched shoe day, my favorite school day of all. I always wear one boot and one flip flop and go flip, clomp, flap all the way down the hall. Now I know what you must be thinking. It sounds not quite right but to get the full affect you will need one left cowboy boot, a little bit loose, and one right flip flop, just a little too tight.

N is for my Nana, the coolest person I know. She tells jokes, jumps rope and roller skates, no one in town puts on a better show. Nana used to perform with the circus but that was a long time ago. She says she's retired but I happen to know, when no one is watching, she still performs the Spinning Tornado!

M

N

O is for Odd, which is exactly what you'll find at Owen J Oswald's rare antiques and Oddities, at the corner of Opossum and Thyme. Inside there are arrows that point right for, 'This way' and left for, 'some of that'. They claim to have it all, pickled gator in a jar, a necklace made from toenails, and at least a dozen rats. But people come from far and wide to see Oswald's truly odd, trio of tap dancing acrobatic alley cats.

P is for Pirates, sailing around the globe. Adventure on the high seas, buried treasure, best friends together, and for sure all that gold! I bet when you're a pirate you don't even need a bath. No bed time, or homework, but we will need to count our treasure, so one of you is still going to have to do math.

Q is for Quarters, like many kids, I would do anything for just a few. Heck I even rescued one in gum that was stuck to a stranger's shoe. You can find change anywhere, all you have to do is look. I once found twenty-four quarters up on a shelf tucked away in a book. Mom said, "Those Quarters were for looking, not touching and one day they would be mine." I told her I was glad to hear that because I'd like to take them to the candy store, I bet they'll spend just fine.

R is for Red Rock Rattlesnake Roping and Rodeo, one night I watched it on tv. Next up to ride was Jeter Jeffery, the toughest cowboy this side of Tennessee. The TV said to stay tuned, so I did, it said this is going to be exciting! To my surprise his big brave horse shot out of the gate like lightning! Sure enough, he roped that cow and waved to the crowd, they said, "He took first place!"

I said, "That's it, I'm gonna be a cowboy!" On second thought, maybe not, I'll stick to something easier, like going to outer space.

S is for Sardines, you know, the tiny, smelly fish in a can. My grandpa says they make a super sandwich, his favorite is sardines and spam. He says, "Mikey come try a bite of this, I swear it tastes just like ham!" I back away slowly, not sure what to say. I just watched my grandpa make a sandwich made from two questionable meats in a can.

T is for Tacos, but they're only free on Tuesdays, unless it's in May, and then it's the third Thursday. Terrence and Tito own Let's Taco 'Bout It truck and salsa bar. They were voted best tacos in town by at least two dozen kids in school so far. Everyone says, "They love the 'Burrito Box', inside every box is a prize." Last week it was taco shaped sun glasses, next week could be anything, every week is a new surprise!

S

T

Tito's Taco Bar
"Let's taco bout it"

U is for Ultimate Wrestling, the Friday night showdown in a cage. The man to beat is the Flying Dutchman. He drops into the ring on a rope in a rage! He's clearly a crowd favorite, this underdog from out of town. Everyone jumps to their feet and shouts, "The unsinkable Flying Dutchman will never be taken down!"

V is for Vacation, every year my family likes to take one. Now we could do a theme park or a road trip, maybe a little fun in the sun but my family has different ideas of how summer vacation should be done. Last year, we packed up the family and camped at Saves A Lot groceries. Everyone split up, grabbed a cart, and searched for discounts ever so closely. This year mom says, "We're really in for a treat, we're headed out of town all weekend for the end of the season white sale. We're all getting new underwear, towels, and sheets!"

W is for Wilderness Woodchuck Boys on an overnight campout in the woods. Gathering and preparing our own food as any good Wilderness Woodchuck should. When the weather turned windy, Walter Simms started to whine. We then packed up our sleeping bags, the soda and the pizza and headed back inside. So maybe we weren't in the wilderness, really it wasn't even a park. But we did stay outside for dinner in the yard, the four of us on our own in the dark.

U

ESSENTIALS   TOWEL AND SHEETS 50% OFF

V

W

X is for X-ray, the photo of my broken arm. The doctor asked, "Where were you when this happened?"

I said, "I was on a school field trip to Xander's petting zoo and goat farm." At the end of the tour, we went in the pen to feed the animals a treat. The goats came running so excited and so fast, I threw the food, turned to run, and tripped on my own two feet. When I hit the ground, I knew I had hurt my arm but I decided to lay there and play dead. I thought I was in real trouble until I started to laugh, something was licking and tickling my head.

Y is for Yoodles, the cutest puppies I've ever seen! My neighbor Mrs. Ridley has a teacup poodle, named noodle, who had puppies with a yorkie named Jelly Bean. Those puppies were so tiny and cute every kid in the neighborhood had to have one. Now when you go outside to play there's oodles and oodles of small barking Yoodles, in fact our neighborhood has never been more fun.

Z is for Zippers, I wish they were everywhere! They have at least a million uses, I've been trying to convince my mom to sew them on to all of my underwear. To my way of thinking, they just make life easy, no messing with buttons, ties or shoe laces. Last week, I was talking to Zoe Jean and she said that she could use some zip-on ballet shoes, she's pretty tired of tying laces in all those places.

CPSIA information can be obtained
at www.ICGtesting.com
Printed in the USA
LVHW070058080920
665299LV00032B/603